ONE RICH RAJAH

ONE RICH RAJAH

A COUNTING BOOK

SHEILA & CHARLES FRONT

Hippo Books
Scholastic Children's Books
London

This book is dedicated to the children of Highlands Infants' School, Redbridge.

Scholastic Children's Books,
Scholastic Publications Ltd,
7-9 Pratt Street, London NW1 0AE, UK

Scholastic Inc.,
730 Broadway, New York, NY 10003, USA

Scholastic Canada Ltd,
123 Newkirk Road, Richmond Hill,
Ontario, Canada L4C 3G5

Ashton Scholastic Pty Ltd,
PO Box 579, Gosford, New South Wales,
Australia

Ashton Scholastic Ltd,
Private Bag 1, Penrose, Auckland,
New Zealand

First published in the UK by
André Deutsch Children's Books 1988
This edition published by Scholastic Publications Limited 1993

Text Copyright ©1988 by Shelia Front
Illustrations Copyright © 1988 by Charles Front

ISBN 0 590 55330 5

Printed and bound by Cambus Litho Ltd., Scotland

All rights reserved

The right of Sheila Front and Charles Front to be
identified as the author and illustrator of this work
respectively has been asserted by them in accordance
with the Copyright, Design and Patents Act 1988.

10 9 8 7 6 5 4 3 2

1 **One rich rajah, elephant riding.**

2 Two striped tigers, can you see them hiding?

3 Three hungry lions with long sharp claws.

4

Four green crocodiles with snapping jaws.

5 **Five pretty butterflies floating on the breeze.**

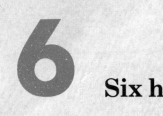

6 Six hissing snakes sliding through trees.

Seven camels wearing veils.

8 Eight proud peacocks spreading their tails.

9 **Nine coloured parrots chattering all day.**

10 Ten naughty monkeys wanting to play.

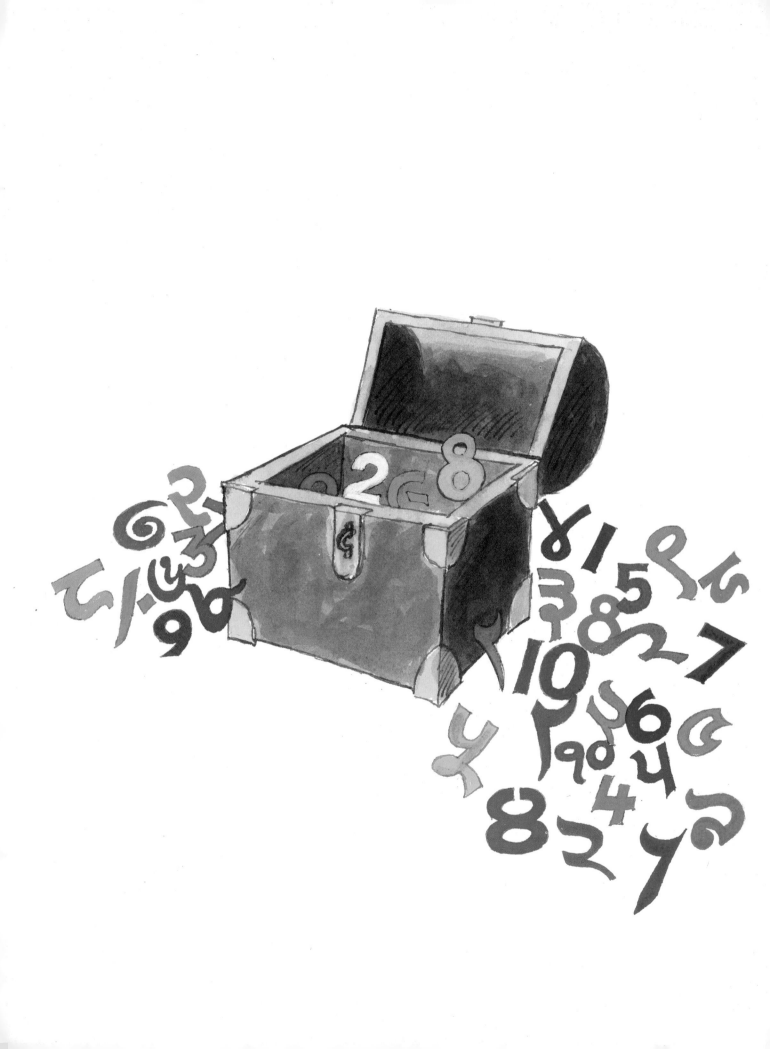